SCOTTI

SCOTTISH ROCKS AND FOSSILS

By Alan and Moira McKirdy
Illustrated by Craig Ellery

Our Rocky Past ... and Present	2	Coal	22
Minerals and Crystals	4	Oil and Gas	24
Rocks from the Fire	6	Rocks Cooked and Squashed	26
Volcanoes	8	Scotland – A Piece of North America	28
New Rocks from Old	10	Wind, Water and Ice	30
Creatures from the Past	12	Age of Ice	32
More about Fossils	14	Life from Rocks?	34
A Race Through Time	16	Rocks at Work	36
Drip, Drip, Drip!	18	Collecting Rocks and Conservation	38
Find that Fossil	20	Places to Visit and Answers	40

Edinburgh : HMSO
Scottish Natural Heritage
National Museums of Scotland

D0257681

OUR ROCKY PAST...AND PRESENT

If we were able to cut a slice out of the Earth, we would see that it is not the same all the way through. The outermost part, beneath our feet, is called the crust. It is very thin compared to the rest of the Earth and forms the continents and the ocean floors. There are many different rocks to be found on the surface of the Earth's crust.

There are many different minerals which go to form this huge variety of rocks but there are only three types of rock.

Igneous rocks are formed when hot, molten material cools down. **Sedimentary** rocks are formed from other rocks which have been broken down into tiny fragments. **Metamorphic** rocks are also formed from other rocks by the action of heat and pressure.

Each rock is a collection of **minerals**. Each mineral is formed from chemicals. For example, one of the commonest minerals, **quartz**, consists of the chemicals **silicon** and **oxygen**.

Scotland's landscape is made of many different rocks. They have been studied by scientists from all over the world. Many important discoveries about the Earth and its structure have been made in Scotland. The study of rocks is called **geology** and the people who study rocks are called **geologists**.

James Hutton (1726–1797) is often described as the father of modern geology. He wrote the first textbook on geology, called *Theory of the Earth*, which was published two years before his death.

Wow! Look at those colours

OUTER CORE

MANTLE

INNER CORE

CRUST

Cut open a peach. Using the illustration of the Earth, try and relate the skin to the crust, flesh to the mantle, stone to the core.

A grain of salt placed on the skin would be much higher than Ben Nevis and a scratch on the surface of the peach would be deeper than Loch Ness.

Ask an adult to cut your peach

MINERALS AND CRYSTALS

We have always been fascinated by minerals. Many are beautiful and some have become very valuable because they are so rare. A good example is a diamond, but none have been found in Scotland ... yet!

Most minerals form deep within the Earth. Here, the temperature is so great that the rocks melt. When they cool, crystals form.

Crystals come in all shapes, sizes and colours. Some are over several metres long, while others can only be seen under a powerful microscope. Each crystal is as unique as a fingerprint, just as each and every snowflake is different from any other.

A crystal consists of tiny particles which arrange themselves in a regular pattern as the crystal grows. This gives the crystal its characteristic shape. Columns, needles, cubes, strands and layers are some of the different shapes or 'habits' that crystals can form. Each has it own typical shape and colour which helps geologists to identify them.

When a crystal grows, it adds layers of chemicals to its surface. Try growing your own crystals of common salt.

Always ask an adult first

1. Dissolve as much salt as you can in a jar of warm water.

2. Let a piece of wool hang from a pencil into the salt water and leave on a window sill.

It's like magic!

3. Tiny salt crystals will begin to grow on the wool. You can also try this experiment with epsom salts.

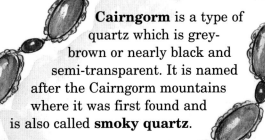

Cairngorm is a type of quartz which is grey-brown or nearly black and semi-transparent. It is named after the Cairngorm mountains where it was first found and is also called **smoky quartz**.

In Scotland, we have many attractive and valuable minerals which are used in jewellery and ornaments.

Garnet is blood-red in colour and is often used in jewellery. It is found in some metamorphic rocks.

Agate is also a type of quartz. It has a banded appearance. It is often cut and the surface polished.

Rocks from the Fire

Deep down in the Earth, the rocks become so hot that they melt. The molten rock which forms deep underground is called **magma**. Over time, magma cools to form solid rocks which we call **igneous** rocks, or 'rocks from the fire'. Scotland has many different types of igneous rocks. When these rocks remain deep within the Earth's crust, they cool very slowly and large crystals form. Granite is a well-known example of igneous rock. Crystals of quartz, feldspar and mica, which make up granite, can grow up to several centimetres in size.

GRANITE

Granites form many kilometres down in the Earth's crust, but if the rocks above are worn away, the granite may appear at the surface. Granites appear at the surface, or **outcrop**, in many different places in Scotland. Geologists mark them in red on a geological map.

Magma can also escape through holes in the Earth's crust and flow over the surface. The molten rock cools very quickly to form lava. Sometimes the magma cools just under the surface, forming sheets of igneous rock. These are called **dykes** and **sills**. Some lavas form columns or rock pillars when they cool. Fingal's Cave on the island of Staffa is a well-known example.

Here is a list of well-known Scottish landmarks which are "made" of granite. Try to match them with the granite splodges.
(Answers on page 40.)

Ailsa Craig
Cairngorm
Lewis & Harris
Arran
Mull
Shetland
Helmsdale,
Sutherland
Skye

THE GRANITE

Volcanoes

A volcano is an opening in the Earth's crust where lava or molten rock can escape. Gas, steam and ash may also be forced out at the same time. Each new outburst of lava is called an **eruption**. The build-up of lava and ash forms the characteristic cone-shape of the volcano. There are many volcanoes in the world where eruptions of lava are still taking place, but do not worry, there are none in Scotland today!

Volcanoes eventually die or become extinct. There are many extinct volcanoes in Scotland. Castle Rock in Edinburgh is part of an extinct volcano. Many millions of years ago, long before there were any people around to watch, two large volcanoes erupted in the area we now know as Edinburgh. Lava poured from the volcanoes and clouds of ash were hurled high into the sky.

The distinctive volcano shape has been worn away over millions of years. The remains of these volcanoes can be seen at Arthur's Seat in Holyrood Park and Castle Rock in Edinburgh. The Pentlands, the Ochil Hills and the Trotternish Ridge on Skye are other examples of hills made of lava from long-extinct volcanoes.

VOLCANIC BOMB

VOLCANIC ASH

LAVA FLOW

EDINBURGH CASTLE ROCK

SILL

DYKE

SIDEVENT

MAGMA CHAMBER

Make yourself a model volcano which really erupts ... messily but safely!

1. Place an egg cup on an upturned yoghurt pot on a tray. Surround with sand.

2. Fill the egg-cup with warm water.

3. Add a few drops of washing-up liquid (foaming agent) plus a few drops of red food colouring (lava colour).

4. Add two teaspoons of cream of tartar followed by one teaspoon of bicarbonate of soda.

5. Stir gently with a lollipop stick and watch your volcano erupt.

WASHING UP LIQUID

FOOD COLOURING

It really works!

New Rocks from Old

Rocks are constantly being worn away into smaller pieces. This is done gradually by wind, rain, frost and snow. Some rocks are fairly soft and break down quite easily, as happens when sandstone cliffs are battered by the sea. Other rocks, like granite, are very hard and resistant to the action of the weather and the sea.

When rocks are broken down, the tiny fragments may be washed away by streams and rivers. Eventually they may reach an inland lake or the sea. We recognise this collection of tiny rock fragments as **sand**, **mud** or **pebbles**.

When the weather is stormy, a great deal of sediment is brought down to the sea by rivers, swollen by rain. Even when rivers or burns are flowing gently, sediment will still be carried to the sea.

As the sediments build up, the lower layers are squashed or **compacted** as more sand and mud is dumped on top. Later, chemicals in the water help to cement together the particles of the compacted sediment so that rocks are formed – new rocks from old! These rocks are called **sedimentary** rocks.

MUD

V

SHELL

Remember that this rock-forming process may take not just thousands but **millions** of years ... and that it is going on all the time!

SANDSTONE

STONE

LIMESTONE

CONGLOMERATE

1. Half-fill a box or tray with sand.

2. Place a piece of card at one end and build the sand up against it to form a slope.

3. Using a spoon, trickle water on to the top of the slope. Notice the path of the water.

4. Repeat, but pour water from a jug. Compare the power of the faster flow and larger volume of water.

CREATURES FROM THE PAST

Fossils are the remains of animals and plants which lived on the Earth millions of years ago. They are very important to us as they help us to work out what the Earth was like long ago. It is like going on a journey back in time. The study of fossils is called **palaeontology**.

When animals or plants die, their bodies usually rot away or may be eaten by other animals. However, if they were quickly covered by sand or mud, for example, by falling into a river or swamp, they may be preserved. If this happened, the dead plant or animal may become **fossilised**.

Fossils are usually found in sedimentary rocks.

The ichthyosaur lived in the sea about 150 million years ago. It had rows of sharp teeth and a streamlined shape similar to a dolphin, but this animal was a reptile. It is nicknamed the 'sea-dragon'.

ICHTHYOSAUR

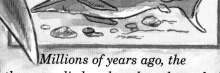

Millions of years ago, the ichthyosaur died and sank to the seabed.

As the body became buried in mud and sand, the flesh rotted away, leaving the skeleton.

As the s... sk...

Fossils of this sea-living relative of the dinosaurs have been found on Skye. Fossil plants found in these rocks suggest that the climate of Skye, 150 million years ago, was more like Barbados than Broadford today!

PLESIOSAUR

You can try to make your own 'mould' fossil.

1. Press your shell into the clay.

2. Carefully remove the shell, leaving an imprint. You have now made your own 'mould' fossil.

3. If you allow the clay to harden, you can add some more clay or even Plaster of Paris into the imprint to make your own 'cast' fossil.

PLASTER OF PARIS

...t turned to rock, so the ...became fossilised.

The rock may then have been eroded so that the fossil became exposed at the surface.

More about Fossils

Not all fossils formed in exactly the same way. Sometimes, after the dead animal had been buried in the sediment, it rotted away, leaving a hole in the rock. This is how a **mould** fossil is formed.

If, however, the hole left in the rock later became filled with sand or mud, this formed a **cast** fossil.

In other cases the remains of the buried animal were gradually replaced with minerals which hardened to form rock.

We can also find footprints, burrows and droppings of animals which are preserved in rock. These are called **trace** fossils.

There are lots of different types of fossils in Scotland.

Find the names of these fossils in the stone carving. *(Answers on page 40.)*

ichthyosaur
plesiosaur
dinosaur
crinoid
ammonite
trilobite
bivalve
fish
water scorpion
graptolite

```
P R G R A P T O L I T E N
L S A B B G O F X H I O J
E A E Z O C R I N O I D H
S S V R W D C S O P C P T
I U L Z K F B H R Q H R W
O L A T R I L O B I T E J
S T V K V H C E G K H U M
A D I N O S A U R M Y L X
U H B V R D N H F I O H K
R P J E N L M R L I S A O
E Q T F E O I Y K R A U S
G A M M O N I T E S U N Y
W B N L F C O S A U R U R
```

Hugh Miller (1802–1856) was a stonemason, writer and geologist, who was born in Cromarty in the north of Scotland. Working with the sandstone of that area, he became fascinated by the many and varied fossil fish he found in the rocks. He wrote popular science books in which he was able to explain his passion for fossils.

15

A Race Through Time

A simplified explanation of the geological time scale.

4,600 million years ago

1,000 m.y.

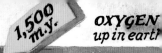

1,500 m.y. OXYGEN up in earth

4,000 m.y.

3,500 m.y.

CAMBRIAN PERIOD – Trilobites.

ORDOVICIAN PERIOD – First corals and graptolites.

SILURIAN PERIOD – Jawless fish appear. Scotland collides with England.

DEVONIAN PERIOD – Fish with armoured heads. Lava flows form Ochil Hills.

CARBONIFEROUS PERIOD Sharks, amphibians, water swamps, crinoids, and coal. "Arthur's Seat" volcano erupts.

PERMIAN PERIOD – Many ancient species become extinct including trilobites. New reptiles appear. Desert conditions in Scotland.

TRIASSIC PERIOD – Desert conditions continue

JUR Warm s... Ammoni.. and plesiosa... Dinosaurs on the

570 m.y. 510 m.y. 438 m.y. 410 m.y. 355 m.y. 290 m.y. 25

– How old are the oldest rocks in Scotland?

– What age is the oldest fossil in Scotland?

– In which period did t... "coal swamps" grow?

16

...rts to build
...nosphere.

Scotland's oldest
fossil (**1,800 m.y.**)

2,000
m.y.

QUATERNARY PERIOD – Ice Age, small mammals, woolly mammoths, wolves & humans.

TERTIARY PERIOD – Plant life continues to flourish. Volcanoes erupt in Skye, Arran, Ardnamurchan and Rum.

CRETACEOUS PERIOD – All dinosaurs become extinct.

...IC PERIOD – ...w seas teeming with life. ...ivalves, ichthyosaurs ...the sea. ...nd.

2 m.y.

2,500
m.y.

65 m.y.

135 m.y.

205 m.y.

Compare geological time with one hour of time. Look at this clock face. If the Earth was formed just after midday, the first animals to leave fossil records didn't appear until seven minutes to one and humans appeared with a fraction of a second to go before one o'clock!

Oldest Rocks
found in
Scotland

3,300
m.y.

3,000
m.y.

– In which period did Scotland
collide with England?

(Answers on page 40.)

DRIP, DRIP, DRIP!

Some rocks are made up of bits of fossils. **Limestones** may consist of the shells of tiny sea creatures or even the remains of coral reefs which lived millions of years ago. Other types of limestone were formed in seawater as calcite (calcium carbonate) was deposited around sand grains, cementing them into a solid rock.

Although limestone is a very tough rock, it has one weakness – it will dissolve very slowly in water. Rainwater is a weak acid and can dissolve limestone more quickly ... but even then, this process takes thousands of years. The results can be spectacular!

Is it limestone?
1. To test whether a rock is limestone, place it on an old plate.

2. Drip strong vinegar on to it.

3. If the rock is limestone, it will 'fizz'. The 'fizz' is carbon dioxide gas, which is produced when the acid of the vinegar reacts with the calcium carbonate of the rock.

Although not common, there are limestone caves in Scotland.

In Sutherland, near Durness, on the north coast, we find Smoo Caves and inland, near Inchnadamph, there are caves at Traligill and Allt nan Uamh, which means 'Burn of the Cave'.

Water continually drips from the cave roof. With each drip, a tiny amount of the dissolved calcite is left behind. This gradually builds up into a **stalactite**.

Large stalactites and stalagmites may take 10,000 years or more to develop, but you can make your own in a couple of days!

The water which drips on to the cave floor will evaporate, leaving a tiny amount of calcite behind. This gradually builds upwards to form a **stalagmite.**

1. Add washing soda to 2 large jars almost full of warm water until no more will dissolve.

2. Place a piece of wool, between the jars, with the ends in the solutions (weight the ends of the wool with a small nut or a paper clip).

3. Place a saucer between the jars and leave for a few days.

Remember, use rubber gloves for this activity

The solution will seep up and along the wool and drip on to the saucer. Each drip leaves behind a little washing soda and so forms a stalactite. As the water evaporates from the drips collecting on the saucer, a stalagmite forms.

FIND THAT FOSSIL

Race your opponents around Scotland, collecting fossils as you go, remembering the 'collecting rules' on pages 38 and 39. The first to finish awards his or her finds to the local museum.

12

SHETLAND – FIND FOSSIL FISH

11

ORKNEY – FIND FOSSIL FISH

ACHANARRAS QUARRY, CAITHNESS

10

FIND FOSSIL FISH

13

EATHIE, SUTHERLAND – FIND AMMONITE

14

ELGIN, MORAYSHIRE – FIND REPTILE FOOTPRINT

9

8

VALTOS, ISLE OF SKYE – FIND DINOSAUR BONE

VALTOS, ISLE OF SKYE – FIND DINOSAUR FOOTPRINT

7

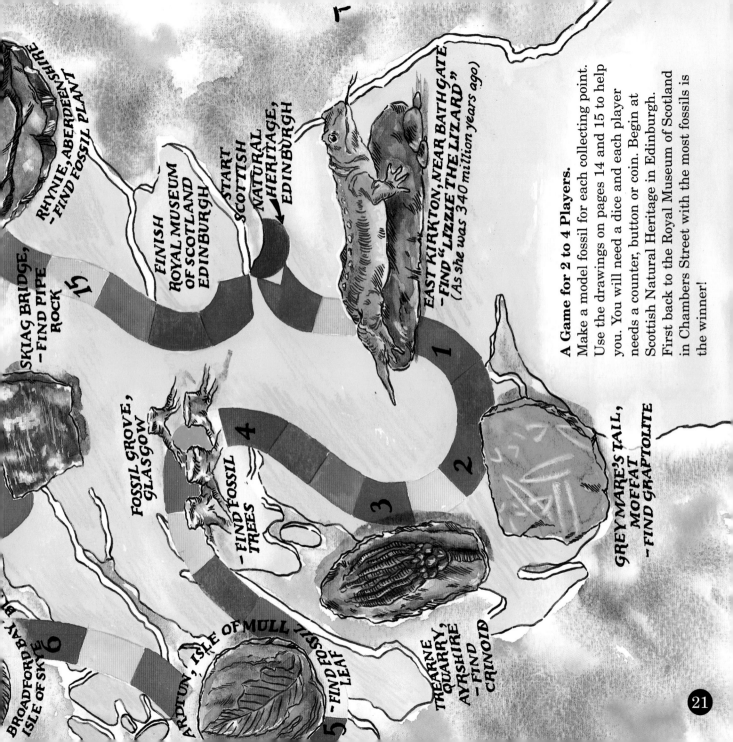

RHYNIE, ABERDEENSHIRE
– FIND FOSSIL PLANT

SKIAG BRIDGE,
– FIND PIPE ROCK

15

FINISH
ROYAL MUSEUM
OF SCOTLAND
EDINBURGH

START
SCOTTISH
NATURAL
HERITAGE,
EDINBURGH

EAST KIRKTON, NEAR BATHGATE,
– FIND "LIZZIE THE LIZARD"
(As she was 340 million years ago)

1

2

3

4

GREYMARE'S TAIL,
MOFFAT
– FIND GRAPTOLITE

FOSSIL GROVE,
GLASGOW

– FIND FOSSIL TREES

TREARNE
QUARRY,
AYRSHIRE
– FIND CRINOID

ARDTUN, ISLE OF MULL
– FIND FOSSIL LEAF

5

BROADFORD BAY,
ISLE OF SKYE

6

A Game for 2 to 4 Players.
Make a model fossil for each collecting point.
Use the drawings on pages 14 and 15 to help
you. You will need a dice and each player
needs a counter, button or coin. Begin at
Scottish Natural Heritage in Edinburgh.
First back to the Royal Museum of Scotland
in Chambers Street with the most fossils is
the winner!

21

COAL

Coal is made from plants which lived about 300 million years ago. When we burn coal, we are releasing the energy which these prehistoric trees trapped from the sun. This process is called photosynthesis. We call coal a **fossil fuel**.

Do you know what photosynthesis is? If not, look it up ... then check your answer on page 40.

At this time, Scotland had a hot and humid climate. Much of the land near the coast was covered by fast-growing swamps. When the trees died, they fell into the shallow swamps, building up a great thickness of rotting vegetation. As more and more material built up, the partly rotted plants became buried and compressed and coal was formed. The sea level rose and fell during these times, and when the oceans covered the coastal plains, thick layers of sands and muds were dumped on top of the layers of coal. When the sea level fell, the swamps would grow again and another layer of coal was in the making.

Fossil Grove at Victoria Park in Glasgow has eleven fossil tree stumps preserved in their growing position. These 300 million-year-old trees have roots and bark, just like the trees in your local park! The only difference is that these trees have turned to stone! Try and imagine the whole park covered by tall trees. You would be up to your knees in a muddy swamp! Yuk!

Wow!! Seriously Carboniferous

Bark rubbing and leaf printing

Compare the patterns produced in this activity with the fossil plants.

OIL AND GAS

Millions of years ago, when Scotland was a tropical paradise, the shallow seas around our shores were teeming with minute animals and plants – similar to the plankton found in the sea today. When these creatures died, they sank to the seabed and were buried by layers of sand and mud. Gradually these sediments turned to rock under their own weight and the decayed remains of the tiny creatures turned into oil and gas. Once formed, the oil and gas rose towards the surface through tiny holes or pores in the rock until trapped by a non-porous layer. This formed an oilfield which now lies far underground waiting to be discovered.

Non-porous layer (NPL) forming oil TRAP

Gas

Oil

Water

Water

Folded Strata (Rock layers)

Fault

NPL

Many important oilfields have been discovered in the North Sea. Oil and gas are brought ashore through long pipelines laid on the seabed. The oil terminal at Sullom Voe on Shetland was built at the end of this pipeline, and it stores the crude oil in enormous tanks ready to be taken to oil refineries.

Crude oil is a mixture of chemicals called **hydrocarbons**. They can be separated at an oil refinery and are used to make lots of useful things such as petrol, paraffin, diesel, lubricating oil, plastics, detergents and paints.

Non-porous layer

Fault

Salt Dome.

NPL

Complete this crossword using these clues:
- Makes things clean
- Popular car fuel
- Heater may burn this
- Lorry fuel
- Toys often made of this
- Protects and decorates
(Answers on page 40)

25

Rocks Cooked and Squashed

Imagine the scene 10 kilometres below your feet. Temperatures deep in the Earth's crust reach a sweltering 500°C (five times hotter than boiling water) and the pressure there would be enough to give you more than a headache. Under these conditions, rocks are cooked and squashed or **metamorphosed**. New minerals are formed in rocks which started out as sediments or lavas. So, new rocks are created from old ones. Many areas in Scotland are made from **metamorphic** rocks.

MARBLE

SCHIST

The Outer Hebrides are made of **gneiss** (pronounced 'nice'), a type of metamorphic rock. These rocks date back about 3 billion years ago to just after the Earth was formed. **Schists** and **marble** are other types of metamorphic rocks which are found particularly in northern Scotland. Most rocks of this type have a banded appearance which developed as a result of intense heat and pressure.

GNEISS

So how can these rocks, formed deep in the Earth crust, now be seen at the surface? Good question. Things have not always been the way we see them today. In Scotland, we have had mountain ranges the size of the Alps which have been worn away by ice, wind and water. All that is left are the deep foundations of these mountains. These rocks were twisted and bent into **folds** and were sliced into sections by breaks in the rock called **faults**.

Remember! Get an adult to help you cut your Plasticine.

Sir James Hall (1761–1832) tried to form metamorphic rock in his foundry. He put powdered limestone in a gun barrel, sealed it to maintain pressure, then placed it in a furnace. The heat and pressure changed the limestone into marble.

Make your own folded and faulted rocks.

1. Build up five layers of coloured Plasticine.

2. Push them into simple folds.

3. Keep pushing to produce overfolds.

4. Using a knife, cut through all the layers. Now push and watch a fault appear!

SCOTLAND – A PIECE OF NORTH AMERICA

Did you know that Scotland was, at one time, part of an area of land which included North America and Greenland? Or that Scotland was separated from England by an ocean, called the Iapetus Ocean, which was wider than the Atlantic? This is not a joke – geologists are sure that it is true. Some rocks found in Scotland are very similar to rocks in Greenland and North America.

The land on the Earth's surface is divided up into plates, which are constantly on the move. Scotland crashed into England about 400 million years ago and we have been stuck together ever since. We were about 20° south of the equator at the time! But we are moving further and further away from America – at about the rate that your toenails grow. Your school atlas is accurate for the minute, but if you lived to be a billion years old, you would see a very different map of the world.

When continents collide, mountain ranges are created. The mountains of Scotland were at one time as high as the highest mountains on Earth, but they have been worn down over millions of years by wind, water and ice.

Iapetus Oce

ENGLAND

Ancient continent of AVALONIA

Ancient continent of LAURENTIA

SCOTLAND

Make a continental jigsaw.

1. With the help of a map of the world, draw or trace the shapes of the continents.

2. Cut out the shapes and try to fit them together e.g. South America, Africa, India, Antarctic and Australia were once joined to form a supercontinent called Gondwanaland.

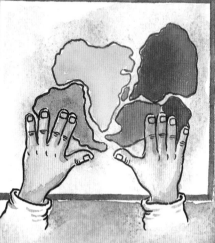

You could even try floating the continents on water to represent the crust 'floating' on the mantle.

WIND, WATER AND ICE

The writing on old gravestones can often be difficult to read, as they have been bombarded for hundreds of years by wind, rain and snow. The rocks beneath your feet have also been exposed to the changing seasons ... but for millions of years. They are heated up by the sun, battered by the wind and rain and frozen by frost, ice and snow. It is no surprise that the rocks eventually break down into smaller pieces by this process of **weathering**.

Rivers carry huge quantities of mud, sand and boulders downstream from the place they were formed. The faster a river flows, the more material it can carry.

Waves along the seashore eat into the rocks and beaches form where sand has been piled up. Seastacks, such as the Old Man of Hoy, have also been formed by the power of the waves.

Wind can whip up sand at the sea shore into sand-dunes.

Ice used to cover the whole of Scotland during the Ice Age and it shaped the landscape to the familiar features we see today. Lucky for us that the climate has warmed up since the Ice Age and the ice has melted.

THE OLD MAN of HOY

That's the real Old Man of Hoy

Rain can also cause rocks to break down into smaller pieces. Rainwater absorbs gases from the air making it a weak acid, which then attacks the rocks. Air pollution makes rain an even stronger acid, which has caused serious damage to old buildings by dissolving the stonework.

When weathered rock fragments are carried away, we call this **erosion**. Erosion has taken place throughout the history of the Earth and is continuing to this day.

Freezing clay to demonstrate freeze-thaw and onion-skin weathering.
You will need 2 lumps of moist clay and some cling-film.

1. Squeeze each lump to remove air bubbles.

2. Wrap each lump in cling-film.

PLACE 1 *in* FREEZER   PLACE 2 *on* WINDOW SILL

3. After a day, remove from freezer and unwrap. Allow to thaw. What happens? (Answer on page 40.)

Hmmm, interesting

Age of Ice

It is almost impossible to imagine, but Scotland was completely covered by a great carpet of ice and snow in the recent geological past. Even the highest peaks of the Cairngorms and Ben Nevis were submerged! We call this time the **Ice Age**.

This great pile of ice and snow finally melted about 10,000 years ago and it was only then that plants could begin to grow again. The land was much changed by the ice and snow. As a **glacier** or 'river of ice' moved, the rocks it contained rubbed against the ground underneath. In this way, glaciers cut into the Earth's surface, forming glens and carving the harder rocks into hills and mountains.

In the Ice Age, it was not cold all the time. During the warmer periods, or **interglacials**, some of the ice melted. But then the snow returned and thick ice sheets covered the land again. This warming up and cooling down happened around fifty times throughout the Ice Age. It seems almost certain the ice will return in the future, but do not worry, it will take another few thousand years for this to happen!

During the Ice Age, many unfamiliar creatures, such as woolly mammoths, brown bears and packs of wolves, roamed the frozen wastes of Scotland in search of food. Our ancestors sheltered from the cold in caves and the layers of soil and debris which collected in these caves tell us a great deal about how they lived and what they ate.

CORRIE

This is a Woolly Mammoth

BOULDER CL

32

MORAINE

This is the work of ice

Louis Agassiz (1807–1873) was a Swiss geologist. While on a visit to Edinburgh, he showed that Scotland had once been covered by ice. After looking at scratches on the surface of a rock at Blackford Hill, in Edinburgh, Agassiz said 'This is the work of ice'.

The debris which a glacier contains creates friction and makes the ice move more slowly.

GRAVEL & WATER

1. Place a handful of gravel in an empty margarine tub and fill with water.

2. Fill a second empty margarine tub with water.

WATER ONLY

3. Freeze both tubs.

4. Remove both frozen blocks and test their 'moving power' down a slope (e.g. wooden plank).

Which moves faster? (Answer on page 40.)

SNOUT

MELTWATER

LIFE FROM ROCKS?

We know that rocks are broken down, by weathering and erosion, into tiny fragments. Plants and animals live on these fragments and, when they die, they decay and form the **organic** (once-living) matter we call **humus**. This enriches the soil and helps to trap air and water which is needed for plants to grow.

Different rocks will produce different mineral particles, and this gives us the variety of soil types.

Topsoil contains organic matter

HELLO

Subsoil made up only of mineral particles

ROCKS

A **clay** soil has a fine texture. It has very small air spaces and, when dry, it appears 'powdery'. When water tries to pass through, it becomes waterlogged, sticky and 'heavy'.

A **sandy** soil has a coarser texture. The air spaces are much bigger than in clay soil so water drains through easily. Sandy soil is said to be 'light'.

A mixture of these two basic soil types is called **loam** and is ideal for growing plants.

There is a variety of soil types in Scotland. The farmlands of the Midland Valley, Borders and Aberdeenshire have a thick layer of fertile loam giving good growing conditions for crops and lush grass for cattle to eat. Compare this with the poor soil of hill farms, where only hardy crops, such as oats, can be grown and grazing is only good enough for sheep.

1 Put 2 or 3 handfuls of soil in a jar

2 Add water until 3/4 full

Leave to settle

3 Screw on lid and shake for one minute

Compare soil samples from different places.

What happens? (Answers on page 40.)

Whoopee!

4

You may find several layers settling out - gravel, sand, silt and clay and even organic material

The heaviest layer forms on the bottom of the jar - what is this?

The lightest layer may float on the water - what is this?

ROCKS AT WORK

For thousands of years, metals have been an important part of everyday life. The ancient tribes of Scotland used metals to make tools and weapons from iron and bronze (an alloy of copper and tin) and jewellery from gold and silver.

These early miners cut tunnels and shafts into the rock as they removed the mineral ore. The Romans found deposits of lead and zinc at a place near Abington. It was later named Leadhills.

The rocks of Scotland continue to yield a variety of essential materials, such as crushed rock for making roads and concrete, coal and oil and gas for fuel. Prospectors have even located some deposits of gold! People have been panning for gold at the Suisgill Burn in Sutherland for many years. One man collected enough gold from here to make his wife's wedding ring.

These natural materials continue to be very valuable to us and we must use them wisely. Your children will want to use these materials too, so we must plan carefully.

Quarries and mines are noisy and dusty places, so we must make sure that they do not damage the countryside when they are working and that the pollution they may cause is cleaned up. Is there a quarry near where you live? If they are properly restored, quarries can become popular spots for wildlife, a place to collect fossils and rocks or a picnic area.

Local stone was often used to build the most beautiful buildings in our towns and cities. Most of the buildings in the New Town of Edinburgh are made of sandstones. Some of these came from Craigleith Quarry which is now the site of a superstore. Much of Aberdeen is built of granite from Rubislaw Quarry.

James 'Paraffin' Young (1811–1883) established the world's first commercial oilworks in 1851. The red shale bings, which are such a feature of West Lothian countryside, are a reminder of this once-thriving industry. From his personal fortune, amassed from paraffin and assorted products, he funded his friend David Livingstone's African explorations.

Choose an interesting building near where you live.

Try to find out what rock type it is made from and where the rock was quarried.

QUARRY IN WORK

QUARRY RESTORED

Boo!

This is the life.

COLLECTING ROCKS AND CONSERVATION

Studying and collecting rocks and fossils is great fun. It takes you out into the fresh air and you can also find out more about your local area or about the places you visit on holiday. There are many places where this can be done safely. The seashore is often rocky and is a good place to start. You can study the rocks in safety, wherever you go, if you follow a few simple rules.

Geologists are sometimes destructive with their hammers, but you need not be! If you must, collect a few small specimens but remember that others will want to make the same discoveries as you have.

Happy hunting!

ALWAYS ASK PERMISSION IF YOU INTEND TO GO ON TO PRIVATE LAND

PRIVATE LAND — TRESPASSERS WILL BE PROSECUTED

BEWARE LOOSE ROCK

Wow!! An example of Cardioceras Densiplicatum

OH NO!

COLLECT SPECIMENS OF ROCKS AND FOSSILS FROM LOOSE MATERIAL AND SCREE RATHER THAN BASH OFF A FRESH PIECE

USE YOUR COMMON TO JUDGE WHETH OF COAST IS SAFE —

Try to identify some rocks and fossils. If you live in a town or city, just look around you – there is geology everywhere! Buildings and bridges are often made of interesting rock. When you are on holiday, pick up a stone or pebble to build up your own collection. Then visit your local museum – you can find out if you have identified these rocks and fossils correctly.

FOLLOW THE COUNTRY CODE

Always take a responsible adult with you

OH NO!!

ENSE AND LOCAL ADVICE
ROCK FACE OR STRETCH
OUBT, GO SOMEWHERE ELSE

PLACES TO VISIT AND ANSWERS

Here is a list of places where you can find out more about Scottish rocks and fossils. Although your local museum may have displays about the geology of your area, the Royal Museum of Scotland in Edinburgh and the Kelvingrove Museum and Hunterian Museum in Glasgow are also well worth a visit, as will be The Dynamic Earth Exhibition, when it opens in Edinburgh in 1997. The museums in Perth and Elgin are also worth a visit.

You will find noticeboards, leaflets or guided tours to explain the geology at the following places.

Knockan Cliff and Inverpolly National Nature Reserve, north of Ullapool

Beinn Eighe National Nature Reserve, near Kinlochewe

Glen Roy National Nature Reserve, near Fort William

Rum National Nature Reserve (visits to be arranged through SNH)

Cairngorms National Nature Reserve

Edinburgh Castle

Holyrood Park in Edinburgh

Traprain Law, near Haddington

St Abbs Head, near Eyemouth

Lady Victoria Colliery – The Scottish Mining Museum, near Newtongrange

Fossil Grove, in Victoria Park, Glasgow

Staffa

Kilt Rock, on Skye

National Trust for Scotland Visitor Centre at Glencoe

Leadhills Mining Museum, near Wanlockhead

The Almond Valley Heritage Trust, near Livingston

The Highland Boundary Fault Trail, at David Marshall Lodge at Aberfoyle

Orkney Fossil and Vintage Centre, Burray, Orkney

Rockwatch - a club for all fans of fossils, rocks and dinosaurs. More information from Watch, The Green, Witham Park, Waterside, South Lincoln LN5 7JR

Answers

Page 6/7: Name the Granites - A Shetland; B Helmsdale, Sutherland; C Lewis & Harris; D Ailsa Craig; E Cairngorm; F Skye; G Mull; H Arran

Page 14/15: Fossil Wordsearch

P	R	G	R	A	P	T	O	L	I	T	E	N
L	S	A	B	B	G	O	F	X	H	I	Ø	J
E	A	E	Z	O	C	R	I	N	O	Ø	D	H
S	S	V	R	W	D	C	S	O	P	C	P	T
I	U	L	Z	K	F	B	H	R	Q	H	R	W
O	L	A	T	R	I	L	O	B	I	T	E	J
S	T	V	K	V	H	C	E	G	K	H	U	M
A	D	I	N	O	S	A	U	R	M	Y	L	X
U	H	B	V	R	D	N	H	F	I	O	H	K
R	P	J	E	N	L	M	R	L	I	S	A	O
E	Q	T	F	E	O	I	Y	K	R	A	U	S
G	A	M	M	O	N	I	T	E	S	U	N	Y
W	B	N	L	F	C	O	S	A	U	R	U	R

Page 16/17:

a) 3,300 million years old
b) 1,800 million years old
c) Carboniferous d) Silurian

Page 22/23: Photosynthesis – green plants can make their own food in their leaves, using light energy from the sun, carbon dioxide from the air and water from the soil.

Page 24/25: North Sea Oil Crossword

		P	A	I	N	T	
					O		
D	E	T	E	R	G	E	N	T
					T		
					H		
D	I	E	S	E	L		
P	A	R	A	F	F	I	N
P	E	T	R	O	L		
					I		
P	L	A	S	T	I		

Page 30/31: In the freezer, the water in the clay turns to ice and expands. This causes the clay to crack.

Page 32/33: The 'glacier' with the gravel moves more slowly because of friction – it may scratch the slope's surface.

Page 34/35: The layers will settle out: gravel, sand, silt, clay with humus on the water surface.

Wow!! Look at those colours!

For my agent, Becky Bagnell. Thank you for your wisdom,
support and friendship. You are awesome! – PB

For Natacha – MB

Bloomsbury Publishing,
London, New Delhi, New York and Sydney

First published in Great Britain in 2015
by Bloomsbury Publishing Plc
50 Bedford Square, London, WC1B 3DP

A CIP catalogue record for this book
is available from the British Library

ISBN 978 1 4088 3903 4 (HB)
ISBN 978 1 4088 3904 1 (PB)
ISBN 978 1 4088 3902 7 (eBook)

Printed in China by Leo Paper Products, Heshan, Guangdong

1 3 5 7 9 10 8 6 4 2

All papers used by Bloomsbury Publishing are natural, recyclable products
made from wood grown in well-managed forests. The manufacturing processes
conform to the environmental regulations of the country of origin

www.bloomsbury.com

BLOOMSBURY is a registered trademark
of Bloomsbury Publishing Plc